Immaculate Misconceptions

The
Geographical
Association

Photo: Roger Carter

Theory
INTO
Practice

PROFESSIONAL DEVELOPMENT
FOR GEOGRAPHY TEACHERS
Series editors: Mary Biddulph and Graham Butt

Immaculate Misconceptions

JANE DOVE

The
Geographical
Association

The author

Dr Jane Dove is Head of Geography at St Paul's Girls' School, Brook Green, London.

The series editors

Dr Mary Biddulph is Lecturer in Geography Education in the School of Education, University of Nottingham and Dr Graham Butt is Senior Lecturer in Geographical Education in the School of Education, University of Birmingham.

ISBN 1 899085 73 4
First published 1999
Impression number 10 9 8 7 6 5 4 3 2 1
Year 2002 2001 2000 1999

Published by the Geographical Association, 160 Solly Street, Sheffield S1 4BF. The Geographical Association is a registered charity: no 313129.

The Publications Officer of the GA would be happy to hear from other potential authors who have ideas for geography books. You may contact the Officer via the GA at the address above. The views expressed in this publication are those of the authors and do not necessarily represent those of the Geographical Association.

Designed by Ledgard Jepson Limited
Printed and bound by Colorcraft Ltd, Hong Kong

Contents

Editors' preface

Theory into Practice is dedicated to improving both teaching and learning in geography. The over-riding element in the series is direct communication with the classroom practitioner about current research in geographical education and how this relates to classroom practice. Geography teachers from across the professional spectrum will be able to access research findings on particular issues which they can then relate to their own particular context.

How to use this series

This series also has a number of other concerns. First, we seek to achieve the further professional development of geography teachers and their departments. Second, each book is intended to support teachers' thinking about key aspects of teaching and learning in geography and encourages them to reconsider these in the light of research findings. Third, we hope to reinvigorate the debate about how to teach geography and to give teachers the support and encouragement to revisit essential questions, such as:

- Why am I teaching this topic?
- Why am I teaching it in this way?
- Is there a more enjoyable/challenging/interesting/successful way to teach this?
- What are the students learning?
- How are they learning?
- Why are they learning?

This list is by no means exhaustive and there are many other key questions which geography teachers can and should ask. However, the ideas discussed and issues raised in this series provide a framework for thinking about practice. Fourth, each book should offer teachers of geography a vehicle within which they can improve the quality of teaching and learning in their subject; and an opportunity to arm themselves with the new understandings about geography and geographical education. With this information teachers can challenge current assumptions about the nature of the subject in schools. The intended outcome is to support geography teachers in becoming part of the teaching and learning debate. Finally, the series aims to make classroom practitioners feel better informed about their own practice through consideration of, and reflection upon, the research into what they do best - teach geography.

Mary Biddulph and Graham Butt
July 1999

Introduction

Identifying and explaining misconceptions is an intrinsically interesting field of research, and an understanding of common student misconceptions is a requirement in teacher training. The TTA *Standards for the Award of Qualified Teacher Status* guidance for novice teachers states they must:

- 'know for their specialist subject(s) students' most common misconceptions and mistakes,
- be aware of, and know how to access, recent inspection evidence and classroom-related research evidence on teaching secondary students in their specialist subject(s), and know how to use this information to improve their understanding' (TTA, 1997, p. 4)

Being aware of student misconceptions and finding strategies to address them, should also be part of more experienced teachers' continuing professional development.

The ideas which students bring to the classroom about a wide range of scientific and geographical concepts (Driver *et al.*, 1985) have been variously referred to as 'misconceptions', 'children's science', 'alternative frameworks', 'preconceptions', 'untutored beliefs', 'intuitive notions' and 'alternative conceptions'. Although debate about which term is most appropriate remains unresolved, the term 'alternative conceptions' is the definition used throughout this book.

The aim of this book is to raise awareness in secondary school geography teachers and students of the nature, extent and causes of alternative conceptions in physical and environmental geography. Chapter 1 discusses definitions used in alternative conceptions and outlines why a study of this topic is important. It also identifies possible sources of alternative conceptions. The following chapters review some of the most common alternative conceptions and the associated understanding students have reached about specific topics. Chapter 2 explores physical geography; Chapter 3 considers natural environments and meteorology; and Chapter 4 looks at selected environmental issues. Some chapters include brief descriptions of specific strategies for helping students overcome their misconceptions. Chapter 5 develops these strategies further and considers the pedagogical implications on more effective teaching and learning methods. Chapter 6 briefly relates this to both geography and the wider curriculum.

As the research findings are explained in each chapter the methods currently used to detect alternative conceptions and bias due to stereotyping are reviewed. Suggestions are made throughout as to how students' alternative conceptions can be used to support the professional development of geography teachers in secondary schools.

Photo: Graham Butt

How to use this book

This book is intended as a practical working document to support the work of individual geography teachers and geography departments in schools. Figure 1 offers guidelines on how individuals and groups of teachers can absorb the issues raised in this book into their work in the geography classroom. Column two consists of a set of strategies on which to build good practice, and is by no means exhaustive.

Type of teacher	Activity
Individual geography teacher Newly-qualified teacher Novice teacher Non-specialist teaching geography	• Enhance personal geographical knowledge and clarify individual misconceptions in aspects of physical geography • Begin to anticipate possible misconceptions held by students and plan lessons to identify and challenge them • Critically evaluate teaching in the light of issues identified in this book
Head of geography department Geography teaching team (including non-specialists)	• Create opportunities via in-service training to share subject knowledge and identify teachers' misconceptions prior to teaching related aspects of the subject • Evaluate current schemes of work to identify opportunities for challenging misconceptions at all levels • Evaluate current textbooks and other resources for possible geographical misconceptions and amend/explain errors • Plan opportunities for ongoing research in the classroom to identify the sources of misconceptions held by students and to identify other possible geographical misconceptions • Liaise with feeder primary schools to support non-specialists teaching geography and to enhance the transition from key stage 2 to key stage 3
Other subject departments within the school	• Liaise with departments, e.g. science and mathematics, to ascertain how certain geography-related concepts are being taught and assessed • Ask for feedback on students' misconceptions identified when teaching related concepts in these departments.

Figure 1: *How individuals and groups can use this book.*

Photo: Chris Garnett

1: Some definitions

The debate over the terminology used to describe students' alternative conceptions continues. However, researchers have reached consensus regarding a number of terms, including the following.

- 'Preconception' describes an incomplete or naive notion held about a topic before any formal teaching has taken place (Kuiper, 1994).
- 'Misconception' is usually applied where students have been exposed to some formal model or theory and have assimilated this incorrectly (Driver and Easley, 1978; Kuiper, 1994). It is also used to describe an incorrect mental construct (Fisher and Lipson, 1986).
- 'Error' is used for an answer that scientists would consider to be incorrect.

Alternative conceptions could be corrected by simply presenting the scientifically-accepted view. However, as Osborne *et al.* (1983) note, once alternative conceptions are embedded in a student's knowledge they are often difficult to change and may persist even after the student has received contradictory information.

Why consider alternative conceptions?

The identification of 'alternative conceptions' is important because research suggests that they can act as barriers to further learning (Ausubel, 1968). For meaningful learning to take place students must be able to attach new information to their existing cognitive framework. Where the framework contains alternative conceptions then the students may learn without understanding. The assumption that landforms of similar appearance have a common origin is one source of alternative conception. For example, if students assume that all conical-shaped hills are volcanic, they may have difficulty accepting that similar-shaped landforms have different origins. Students develop alternative conceptions in physical and environmental geography for a variety of reasons. Figure 2 shows some of these reasons, together with specific examples. For a more detailed discussion of the reasons behind alternative conceptions see Dove, 1998a.

Imprecision in the use of scientific terms

Example: the term 'alluvium' generally refers to all unconsolidated material from rivers, but a more restricted view is that it includes only silt-sized particles (Whittow, 1984). Also alluvium is normally applied to material deposited by running water, not lake or marine sediments (Goudie *et al.*, 1994).

Applying broad generalisations to specific cases

Example: assuming all shallow soil profiles are young, whereas in deserts, for example soils are thin and old because little weathering can take place. Similarly to assume that all water runs downhill, whereas this is not always the case: in limestone areas water is held within a closed system and responds to a subterranean fissure system, rather than to a unified regional groundwater pattern (Nelson *et al.*, 1992).

Failing to recognise that definitions change over time

Example: the term 'desert' was originally confined to hot, arid areas, but now encompasses mid-latitude basins and cold areas with low temperatures and physiological drought, rather than any deficiency in precipitation. Similarly the term periglacial was originally applied to processes operating in the cold, dry zone adjacent to a Pleistocene ice sheet, but now it includes non-glacial processes and features of climates, regardless of age or proximity to ice sheets.

Confusing closely related concepts

Example: 'Porous' and 'permeable'. Permeable refers to the ease with which a liquid/gas can pass through a rock or soil, whereas porous refers to the volume of water which can be held within a rock/soil expressed as a ratio of the voids (pores) to the total volume of the material.

Assuming landforms of similar appearance have the same origin

Example: Assuming all conical hills are volcanic, whereas they could be oil or salt domes, steep anticlines, or tower and cone karst scenery.

Assuming that landforms of similar appearance are made of the same materials

Example: Assuming all tors (steep-sided residual hills) are made of granite, whereas they also form in other rock types such as sandstone.

Assuming that specific landforms have only one form

Example: Assuming that all mountain summits are pointed.

Associating rocks with specific colours

Example: Assuming that all limestone is yellow in colour so that grey and white varieties are not recognised.

Assuming landforms are a certain size

Example: Assuming that basalt columns are bigger than they really are. Similarly to believe that drumlins and roche moutonnées are larger than they really are.

Equating specific landforms with particular locations

Example: Associating inselbergs with deserts, whereas they also occur in savanna areas. Similarly to assume that all V-shaped valleys and waterfalls are found in upland sections of a river, whereas they can also occur in lowlands where there has been sufficient elevation such as in a coastal area which has been uplifted from the sea.

Assuming current processes produced present landforms

Example: Many desert landforms, for example wadis, owe their origin to past fluvial events rather than present day processes. Similarly, most of our modern streams are misfits of larger valleys developed during periods of higher discharge.

Constructivism

Constructivists believe that learners do not passively receive information, rather they actively construct knowledge from what they perceive. Piaget carried out pioneering work on children's alternative conceptions about a range of natural phenomena, including mountains, rivers and the weather (Piaget, 1929, 1930). However, Driver and Easley's (1978) work on children's perceptions of particular concepts in science in the 1970s is widely taken as marking the beginning of the 'constructivist movement' in science education. This work stimulated further research into primary, secondary and tertiary students' alternative conceptions of a wide variety of scientific concepts. Some research overlaps with the content taught in geography - for example, work on students' ideas about food chains (Barman et al., 1995).

During the 1990s the constructivist movement in science education came under criticism. Johnson and Gott (1996) questioned the validity and reliability of the student responses; Solomon (1994) raised a number of general concerns including whether, in an interview situation, students simply invented answers to satisfy the questioner. I would argue that geography teachers can gain insights into learning by investigating students' alternative conceptions.

Key ideas

- Students actively construct knowledge and ideas from their perceptions.
- Incorrect mental constructs have been variously referred to as 'misconceptions', 'preconceptions' and 'alternative conceptions'.
- Students bring alternative conceptions to the classroom.
- Alternative conceptions can impede further learning.
- Geography teachers can research these conceptions in the classroom as part of their continuing professional development.

Figure 2: Common sources of alternative conceptions.

Photo: Des Bowden

2: Physical geography 2

This chapter describes some alternative conceptions of rock types, the differences between weathering and erosion, meteorology, rivers and glaciation.

Rock types

Research into students' recognition of rock types has offered insights into the causes of alternative conceptions. In one study (Dove, 1996a) students identified a piece of slate as a sedimentary rock, rather than a metamorphic one, simply because it contained layers. A student called a polished specimen of granite 'marble' because of its smooth appearance; a specimen of grey limestone went unrecognised because students assumed that limestone was always yellow in colour; and a specimen of raw anthracite was not identified because students assumed that coal occurred only in neat nuggets. In each case an incorrect mental construct formed the basis of the alternative conception.

Chapter 5, pages 35-40, offers examples of how the teacher can correct these misconceptions.

Weathering and erosion

The terms 'weathering' and 'erosion' often confuse students because both processes are concerned with the lowering of the land surface and operate over a long time period. Moreover, although students often believe weathering is a pre-requisite to erosion, in reality both processes operate together and are dependent on each other. This makes the individual processes difficult to isolate.

- Many students regard actions such as 'wind abrasion' and 'raindrop erosion' as forms of weathering rather than erosion. This is because they see the processes as related to elements of the weather.
- Students classify processes which have nothing to do with the weather, such as salt crystallisation, as types of erosion.
- Some students regard all erosional processes as physical, which means that they classify corrosion as a type of chemical weathering.
- A number of students believe that all weathering processes are chemical and thus 'ignore' physical processes such as frost- shattering and root-wedging.

My own research into students' ideas about 'weathering' and 'erosion' provides evidence of further examples of alternative conceptions (Dove, 1997a). For example, definitions found in secondary school textbooks may give rise to some of these misconceptions. Some textbooks define erosion in a narrow sense by linking it with movement (Collard, 1988; Waugh, 1990). A broader, more accurate, but less widely known, definition of erosion can be found in *The Encyclopedic Dictionary of Physical Geography*:

'The group of processes whereby debris or rock material is loosened or dissolved and removed from any part of the Earth's surface. It includes weathering, solution, corrasion and transportation' (Goudie *et al.*, 1994, p. 186).

Inadequate textbook definitions often arise from authors' attempts to make geographical concepts more accessible to students; in fact, through, the brevity of these definitions can be the cause of students' misconceptions of physical processes. You can identify and counter these misconceptions in a number of ways - see page 38.

Meteorology

Alternative conceptions are also present in meteorological studies (Dove, 1998b). Moyle's (1980) investigation of 8-16 year-olds' understanding of the weather in New Zealand revealed that students found the concepts associated with atmospheric pressure difficult to understand. Moyle suggested this could be partly attributed to the fact that pressure (unlike rain and wind) is not normally detected by the senses at ground level. More specifically, Moyle found that students appeared to have problems understanding synoptic charts. Many of the students suggested that 'H' meant that 'it was going to be hot' or 'high winds', and 'L' was interpreted as 'it was going to be cold' (rather than indicating high and low pressure). Few of the students were able to offer ideas as to what 'the lines' (isobars) represented. Some thought the lines were something to do with the wind, while others suggested they were heat lines. Moyle also found that students associated the numbers on the charts with temperature or wind speed, rather than pressure (Moyle, 1980). Part of a study of 13-18 year-old students in the USA (Aron *et al.*, 1994) revealed the following alternative conceptions:

- Slightly more than half thought that visible clouds were made of water-vapour, rather than water droplets and ice crystals.
- Nearly two-thirds believed that humid air was heavier (more dense) than dry air.
- Just over half mistakenly thought that air pressure increased, rather than decreased, with height.

From my experience as an assistant examiner marking GCSE and A-level scripts I have observed that students avoid answering questions on meteorology. This suggests that there is considerable scope for identifying and correcting alternative conceptions about this topic. Topics worthy of teacher investigation could include students' ideas about:

- mid-latitude depressions,
- the Coriolis force,
- the seasons, and
- lapse rates.

Further suggestions for investigating misconceptions about meteorology can be found on page 39.

Rivers

According to *Geography in the National Curriculum (England)* (and that for Wales) teachers of geography can develop the 'rivers' topic from key stage 1 through to GCSE and beyond (DES, 1995). Research indicates that from a young age children develop alternative conceptions about rivers and their processes. For instance, many 9-11 year-olds believe that mountain streams flow faster than lowland rivers (Dove *et al.*, in press), whereas in fact velocity remains constant or increases slightly along the course of most streams/rivers (Carlston, 1969). An upland stream has one 'thread' of rapidly flowing water, but its average velocity may be less than that of a lowland river. This is because generally less of the water in a lowland river is in contact with its bed and banks and thus there is less friction between the two (Collard, 1988). Encouraged perhaps by textbooks, primary pupils give two main reasons for believing that mountain streams flow faster than lowland rivers: the water in a mountain stream appears 'frothy' and that water should 'run fast downhill' (Dove *et al.*, in press). Such textbooks often describe river development in terms of Davis's (1899) three-stage cycle of erosion, which perceives:

1. mountain streams as 'youthful',
2. meandering rivers which fill valleys as 'mature', and
3. very broad rivers winding across featureless floodplains as 'old'.

This concept is further reinforced by popular children's literature, for example, in *The House at Pooh Corner* a river is described as follows:

'by the time it came to the edge of the forest the stream had grown-up, so that it was almost a river, and being grown up, it did not run or jump and sparkle as it used to do when it was younger, but moved more slowly' (Milne, 1973, p. 89).

Strategies for identifying and countering the alternative conceptions which students have constructed about rivers are described on page 37.

Glaciation

As glaciation is often not covered at GCSE and is optional in many A-level syllabuses it is a good topic for exploring preconceptions. Before Louis Agassiz published his theory of glaciation (Agassiz, 1838), geomorphologists had long been puzzled by large blocks of granite and schist on the south-east flanks of the Jura Mountains when the bed-rock was composed principally of limestone. Some workers suggested the blocks were the result of volcanic explosions, others thought they had been brought down in a flood, while yet others thought the boulders, which had been found scattered across northern Europe, had drifted in on icebergs (Figure 3). Agassiz and others provided the current explanation for these features by proposing that glacial ice had extended to the areas now free of ice; this changed the way landscapes were perceived. Nevertheless, those students who do possess a limited knowledge of glaciation often mistake drumlins for hills and aretes for mountain ridges, and a vague understanding may also encourage them to incorrectly attribute a variety of landforms to 'the Ice Age'.

Figure 3: *Lyell's explanation for erratics and glacial drift. Charles Lyell believed that erratics and glacial drift were brought by icebergs. His ideas were partly influenced by Darwin's accounts of boulders on icebergs in the South Atlantic.*

Figure 4 provides ideas for exploring and recording students' preconceptions about the last glaciation and its effects.

Britain during the last Ice Age

1 Mark on a map how far you think the ice extended over Britain during the last Ice Age.

2 When do you think the last Ice Age began and finished?

began _____ finished _____

3 Were humans around during the last Ice Age?

yes _____ no _____ not sure _____

4 How deep do you think the ice was?

Was everything covered? _____

5 What do you think glacier ice looked like? _____

_____

(Students may think that glacier ice looks like something out of the fridge clear and clean, whereas in reality it is dirty and largely composed of pressurised snow (Collard, 1988)).

6 Can you name any landforms or famous landscape features which you think might have been created by the Ice Age? _____

Figure 4:

Exploring students' preconceptions about the Ice Age.

Limestone denudation

Students are often confused about the correct use of terminology when studying limestone denudation (Viles, 1993). Some students regard the breakdown and removal of calcium carbonate from limestone pavements as a type of weathering (Dove, 1998c), whereas geomorphologists prefer to describe this process as 'denudation' because both weathering (breakdown *in situ*) and erosion (removal of debris in solution) are involved (Trudgill, 1985; Viles, 1993; Goudie, 1995).

Most students also identify as 'carbonation' the specific process which describes the breakdown and removal of calcium carbonate from limestone pavements (Dove, 1998c). This confusion may arise because the term is frequently used in secondary school textbooks (Clowes and Comfort, 1982); whereas, in fact both carbonation and solution are introduced. The process can be summarised simply as:

Stage 1: carbon dioxide dissolves in rainwater to produce carbonic acid *(solution)*.
Stage 2: the carbonic acid attacks rocks containing calcite, potassium and sodium (in the case of calcite) *(carbonation)*.
Stage 3: the reaction produces calcium hydrogen carbonate (in the case of calcite) and this is then removed in solution by percolating water *(solution)*.

From this it can be seen that both carbonation and solution are involved.

Some students also appear uncertain about the operation of acids on limestone pavements, believing that the acid attacking the limestone is sulphuric rather than carbonic (Dove, 1998c). They may be confusing carbonation with the effects of acid rain. For this reason it is important to ensure that students do not associate carbonation with acid rain. Students should also be made aware that carbonation can affect rocks other than limestone: for example, it may occur as part of granite weathering. Potassium-rich feldspars in granite undergo hydrolysis, one product of which is potassium hydroxide. Carbonic acid then reacts with the potassium hydroxide and carbonation occurs. This reaction creates potassium carbonate which is removed in solution by percolating rainwater.

Questions on limestone denudation could uncover two other preconceptions:

1. The extent to which students recognise that, although it tends to be associated with solutional processes, limestone is also subject to processes such as frost-action, root-wedging and abrasion.
2. Whether students realise that although dissected pavements are a very distinctive feature of limestone, they are essentially glacially- scoured platforms and can develop on other rocks, e.g. sandstone and igneous rocks (Trudgill, 1985).

For strategies to investigate students' alternative conceptions of limestone denudation, see page 38.

Key ideas

- There are many different causes of alternative conceptions in physical geography.
- False assumptions about the size, shape and colour of rock types commonly result in false identification.
- Alternative conceptions are common in weather and climate.
- Weathering and erosional processes are commonly confused.
- Students' ideas about many topics in physical geography have yet to be researched.

Photo: Jane Dove.

3: Natural environments

This chapter considers students' alternative conceptions about natural environments, with special reference to hot and cold deserts and the species associated with them. It also considers potential teaching approaches to identifying students' alternative conceptions.

Although work has been undertaken with primary school pupils, little research has probed secondary students' perceptions of natural environments. Findings suggest that 7-11 year-olds hold very negative views about wetlands; researchers propose that these views may reflect the way these environments are portrayed in children's literature (Anderson and Moss, 1993). Children's perceptions of rainforests focus on the animal life and largely ignore the plant diversity (Greaves *et al.*, 1993; Strommen, 1995). Strommen (1995) found that pupils also confuse temperate with tropical forests and think that rainforests are being destroyed by acid rain. Rainforests are a popular topic at secondary level and, therefore, the topic warrants further teacher investigation.

Deserts

Another natural environment which is commonly covered in the secondary curriculum is hot deserts.

Hot deserts

In some geography textbooks deserts are often described in a stereotypical fashion as landscapes full of sand dunes and cacti (Collard, 1988; Waugh, 1990). But do students believe this? To test this theory, 70 undergraduate students (most without A-level geography) were asked to undertake three activities.

1. **Word association:** they were asked to provide ten words which they associated with the term 'desert' (Dove, 1998d).

2. **Ranking photographs:** the undergraduates were presented with six images (showing a stony desert, a rocky desert, a desert with sand dunes, mesa and buttes, an inselberg and a desert dominated by saguaro cacti), they were then asked to rank these photographs from 'the most' to 'the least' like their own image of a desert.

3. **Names:** the undergraduates were encouraged to name any deserts they knew.

The most popular image selected was that of a desert with sand dunes and, interestingly, terms such as 'sand' and 'dunes' were frequently mentioned in the word associations. The prevalence of a 'Saharan stereotype' was further evident in the high incidence of terms such as 'palm trees', 'oases', 'camels' and, to a lesser extent, 'cacti', 'tents' and 'pyramids' in the word association exercises. The Sahara was the most commonly named desert, followed by the Gobi. The photograph of the saguaro landscape (page 20) did not rate as a popular image of a desert, in fact many students believed that the saguaro grew in flat, sandy terrain, devoid of other vegetation.

Contrast these perceptions with reality:

- Only 30 per cent of the Sahara and Arabia deserts are sandy - instead half of the world's deserts are rocky. Yet the 'Saharan' image dominates many students' conceptions of deserts.

- The saguaro can only survive by storing water and cannot last indefinitely, so flourishes either where there are two rains per year or where fog is present. In fact the saguaro prefers well-drained soil and grows best on gravelly slopes rather than flat surfaces.

- In the USA its human-like silhouette has become a symbol for many desert-like regions but, its distribution is limited to the extreme south-east of California, south-central Arizona and the western portion of the state of Sonora in Mexico.

- It is not found in northern Arizona because it is sensitive to frost.

An examination of junior and lower secondary school textbooks which include images of deserts would seem to confirm the undergraduate students' observations. This is despite the fact that some authors (e.g. Jennings, 1989) warn their readers that not all deserts are full of sand. A lack of space and limited budgets (and perhaps the fact that images of bare expanses of rocky waste do not sell books) often prevents illustrators from portraying the considerable variety found in desert landscapes. The undergraduate students explained that other sources played a part in their often stereotypical conceptions of deserts. As well as the illustrations of deserts in textbooks, students based their ideas on biblical images and popular films such as *The English Patient*.

Textbooks also tend to focus on spectacular landforms such as zeuges (tables of harder rock perched on pinnacles of softer rock), yardangs (aerodynamically-shaped desert landforms) and barchans (crescent-shaped sand dunes) at the expense of ubiquitous features, such as desert pavements. This approach may be rooted in the fact that early studies of desert geomorphology focused on individual, exotic features (Cooke et al., 1992). In reality landforms such as barchans are rare: they occur as isolated features on flat bedrock surfaces where the wind constantly blows from one direction and where the sand supply is limited. Barchans are common only in the Imperial Valley in California and in the Atacama and Egyptian deserts.

Cold deserts

Students harbour misconceptions of cold as well as hot deserts (Dove, 1997b). Images of flat, snow covered Antarctic 'wastes' often lead students to believe there is no landmass beneath the snow and ice. The large quantities of snow on the surface, together with published accounts of Robert Falcon Scott's last expedition to the Antarctic, reinforce the misconception that precipitation is high. In fact the low temperature at the Poles reduces the humidity of the air so that snowfall is very light. Low temperatures also prevent any snow from melting, so it accumulates on the surface giving the illusion of high snowfall.

Further student misconceptions of cold deserts are associated with the species that live in them. Polar bears do not live in Antarctica, as the name of the continent reveals ('anti' = opposite, 'arkos' = the bear). Similarly, although penguins are not found in the Arctic, people frequently believe that they are.

Identifying alternative conceptions

To identify alternative conceptions of natural environments, start by exploring students' knowledge and experience of specific environments. Use a variety of questions, for example, ones on heathland could include:

- How do you define a heathland?
- Is a bracken-infested hillside a more appropriate image of a heathland today than a purple, heather-covered moor?
- How might you distinguish between heath and moorland? (True heaths are found between 50-60° north, usually at less than 200m above sea-level, whereas moorland is found in wetter environments between 250m and 1000m.)

Methods

Common research methods used to detect alternative perceptions of natural landscapes include word associations, drawings and photographs.

Word associations

Word associations on natural environments are easy to administer and quickly generate data (Preece, 1978). However, you should ensure adequate prior instruction to avoid 'chaining' (where the previous response rather than the key word becomes the stimulus for the next response). In addition, where the word associations are to be written on a resource sheet, the number of spaces after the key word will dictate how many words the students supply.

Tabulation of the responses will highlight the most frequently occurring word associations as well as the inappropriate ones. Discuss the results with students in a follow-up lesson and focus on why they think some associations were so popular. You could also use this opportunity to explain why some terms were inappropriate.

This approach can also be used in a range of other contexts, e.g. to investigate students' conceptions of weathering and erosion processes.

Photographs

Photographs are commonly used in geography classrooms to assess students' landscape preferences (Herzog, 1985). As the images selected reflect the teacher's preferences, it is advisable to work with a colleague to evaluate each photograph: two 'judges' will reduce the possibility of bias. You should also consider scale and subject - the inclusion of small-scale features in the image can lead students to draw incorrect conclusions (Dove *et al.*, in press). Confusion may arise over the relative scale of different sized features, and the direction/orientation from which the photograph was taken can also cause problems for students when they 'read' the image.

Drawing

- the openness of the technique makes it difficult to score reliably,

- some concepts (for example, air pollution) are not easy to present in diagrammatic form and, therefore, may be under-represented,

- what students draw will be limited by their ability: students may well leave something out either because they cannot draw it or they feel disinclined to bother, and

- where students decide to start on the paper can influence how they use the available space (Dove, 1997c).

Drawing and sketching taps students' holistic understanding and prevents them from feeling constrained by trying to match their knowledge with that of the teacher (White and Gunstone, 1992). Students occasionally find it easier to convey their understanding of a concept in a visual rather than a written form. There are, however, a number of disadvantages to using student drawings to identify alternative conceptions, for example: Teachers need also to be aware that students may employ symbolism in their drawings to communicate a simple concept, rather than what they really believe. For example, if you ask students to draw a mountain landscape they may well produce a series of sharp pointed triangles representing summits with snow on, but will explain that they know mountains are not really like this. To reduce the chance of misinterpretation of a student's drawing and to clarify any ambiguities, carry out brief follow-up interviews with each student.

The limitations of all these research techniques need to be taken into consideration, especially when interpreting students' perceptions of landscapes. However, you can and should consider how to research your students' alternative conceptions in order to then set about correcting any errors in understanding.

Key ideas

- Students have alternative conceptions about rainforests and deserts.

- Textbook illustrations, film, television and children's literature all help to reinforce stereotypical images of natural environments.

- Perceptions of natural environments can be investigated through word associations, monitoring reactions to photographs and encouraging students to draw them.

Photo: Jane Dove.

4: Environmental issues

This chapter reviews research into students' alternative conceptions of a range of environmental issues. The greenhouse effect, ozone depletion and acid deposition are discussed and the information provided here can form the basis of factual knowledge from which teachers can challenge students' misconceptions of the topic. The chapter concludes with a brief discussion of appropriate methods for probing students' alternative conceptions of environmental issues.

In the mid-1990s several studies monitored primary, secondary and tertiary students' understanding of a variety of scientific concepts which can be related to geography (Boyes and Stanisstreet, 1992, 1997; Boyes et al., 1995, 1996; Christidou and Koulaidis, 1996; Dove, 1996b). Some of the students' alternative conceptions can be traced to the general concern about 'green issues' (especially those related to the atmosphere) which were common in the 1980s.

In the 1980s a series of hot summers raised public awareness about the so- called 'greenhouse effect'. This coincided with media coverage of the 'discovery' of a 'hole' in the ozone layer, and together these factors raised public awareness of the dangers of chloro-fluorocarbons. A simultaneous rise in the number of cases of skin cancer further heightened concern over the depletion of the ozone layer. Road traffic congestion in urban areas and on motorways increased the risk of air pollution and damage to health. The detrimental effects of acid deposition on trees, lakes and public buildings was also a concern.

The greenhouse effect

The term 'greenhouse effect' derives from the concept that carbon dioxide and other greenhouse gases are almost transparent to incoming, short-wave solar rays, but absorb outgoing, long-wave terrestrial radiation.

Most secondary and tertiary students, in accepting the anthropogenic explanation for the intensified greenhouse effect, appreciate that global climate change is a consequence of burning fossil fuels and increased vehicle emissions. These students also understand that global climate change makes the world hotter and the main gas responsible for this is carbon dioxide (Boyes and Stanisstreet, 1992; Dove, 1996b). These students also recognise that higher global temperatures will lead to a melting of the ice caps and subsequent coastal flooding.

Students develop a number of misconceptions related to global climate change (Boyes and Stanisstreet, 1992, 1997; Dove, 1996b). These include:

- Believing that the heat from exhausts, rather than the carbon dioxide, is responsible for the greenhouse effect.

- Thinking that radioactive waste and acid rain also contribute to global climate change.

- Concluding that the greenhouse effect is explained by ozone layer depletion. A common notion is that 'holes' in the ozone layer are responsible for the warming trend.

- Believing that the greenhouse effect leads to an increase in skin cancer.

Ozone depletion

The atmospheric 'ozone layer' has a higher concentration of ozone (O_3) than other atmospheric 'layers' within the stratosphere. Maximum concentrations of ozone are found about 25km above the Equator and between 16-18km above the North and South Poles.

Most students are familiar with where and what the ozone layer is (Boyes et al., 1996). They are also aware that the ozone layer protects the Earth from over-exposure to ultra-violet radiation (Boyes and Stanisstreet, 1992; Dove, 1996b) and are very familiar with the idea that chloro-fluorocarbons are responsible for ozone layer depletion. However, many students believe that destruction of the rainforest, and factory and vehicle emissions, are responsible for the degradation of the ozone layer, and some think that heat and carbon dioxide from vehicle exhausts are responsible for this damage.

Almost all students know that ozone layer depletion will lead to an increase in skin cancer (Boyes and Stanisstreet, 1997; Dove, 1996b). However, few of them realise that ozone layer depletion will also lead to other problems, such as eye irritations and damage to crop growth (Boyes and Stanisstreet, 1997). Although most students know that ozone occurs naturally, few of them realise that volcanic eruptions, lightning and variations in solar radiation contribute to fluctuations in the ozone layer.

A number of questions could be used to explore students' ideas about the ozone layer. For example:

- Do students realise that some ultra-violet radiation is important for synthesis of vitamin D in the human body?

- Do students recognise that, in addition to protecting the Earth from ultra-violet radiation, the ozone layer plays an important part in containing atmospheric circulation and weather patterns?

The ozone layer becomes warm by absorbing ultra-violet rays; a reaction which creates a temperature inversion. This inversion acts like a lid, trapping moisture below it and enabling cloud formation and precipitation. Weakening this lid would alter the Earth's climate and weather patterns: although more ultra-violet rays would reach the Earth (causing warming), this would be countered by cooling in the stratosphere and a reduction in global temperature (Elsom, 1991).

Further questions could concentrate on students' ideas about the ozone hole which forms in spring over Antarctica. Most students know it exists but do not realise it is seasonal. The hole appears in late August and is at its maximum during September and October. By December the springtime circumpolar vortex, which isolates the stratospheric Antarctic air from the rest of the southern hemisphere, breaks down and air from outside this system enters it, causing the ozone hole to dissipate.

Some scientists have linked the appearance of a hole in the ozone layer to the production of chloro-fluorocarbons, but the evidence for this is not conclusive. However, if this is the case, what explanations can students offer for its occurrence so far from the areas where chloro-fluorocarbons are produced? The hole appears over Antarctica because free nitrates bind to the surface of water in high-level ice clouds (termed 'polar stratospheric clouds'). In other parts of the atmosphere free nitrates combine with chlorine to create inactive chlorine nitrate. Therefore, over Antarctica the chlorine is available to split the ozone molecule to create oxygen and thus deplete the layer of ozone.

Students have difficulty distinguishing between stratospheric- and photochemically-produced tropospheric ozone (Dove, 1996b). Stratospheric ozone is produced naturally when sunlight splits the oxygen molecule which then combines into ozone; whereas photochemical tropospheric ozone is produced when sunlight reacts with nitrogen oxide, hydrocarbons and carbon dioxide. Ozone is usually found at high levels in the stratosphere however, during periods of turbulence (such as when a cold front passes), natural incursions of ozone-rich air briefly penetrate to the Earth's lower atmosphere.

You may find that students are confused by the tendency for central urban areas to have slightly lower levels of photochemical ozone than suburbs or rural areas. There are two main explanations for this:

1. Ozone takes time to form so it may have drifted away from the city centre before becoming concentrated in one area.
2. Nitric oxide, which is emitted from vehicle exhausts, destroys newly- formed ozone.

'Acid rain'

'Acid rain' is the term used to describe rainwater with a pH of less than 5-5.6 (Elsom, 1991). Research suggests that most students realise that acid deposition results from burning fossil fuels, but their knowledge of the gases involved in the formation of acid rain is poor (Dove, 1996b). Discussing these concepts, most students refer to sulphur dioxide and a few to nitrogen oxide. Furthermore, Boyes et al. (1996) found that some students believe that carbon dioxide emissions from vehicle exhausts cause acid deposition.

Students appear uncertain whether acid deposition can be produced naturally. Although some students correctly surmise that forest fires may produce sulphur (which combines with precipitation to produce weak sulphuric acid), they do not mention other sources of sulphur production (for example, volcanic eruptions). In reality, all precipitation is likely to be slightly acidic; this is because atmospheric carbon dioxide combines with water droplets to produce weak carbonic acid, and nitric acid is generated during thunderstorms.

The effects of acid deposition

All secondary students are aware that some rock types are more susceptible to the effects of acid deposition than others. However, some students believe it is the softness of the rock rather than its calcium or magnesium content that determines its susceptibility to this type of weathering.

Although most students recognise that acid deposition may have destroyed trees in Scandinavia, only some can offer reasons for this. Some mention that westerly winds carry pollutants to Scandinavia, but very few students mention how the acid nature of the indigenous rock types enhance the effects of acid deposition.

As with global climate change, some aspects of students' understanding of acid deposition are worthy of further investigation. For example:

- Are students aware that the pH scale is logarithmic, which means that each whole number increment represents a tenfold change in acidity?
- Do students realise that the term 'acid deposition' includes dry deposition (i.e. gas directly reacting with stone) as well as wet deposition (i.e. acid rain on stone)?
- What are students' perceptions of the effects of acid deposition on trees?
- Do they, for example, focus on damage to leaves, rather than changes in soil (which in turn can affect the trees in many ways).

Acid deposition damages leaf tissue and leaches nutrients from leaves. However, damage to vegetation is also caused by an increase in the acidity of the soil: acid soil encourages leaching of nutrients from vegetation. It does so by mobilising aluminium (which damages roots) and reduces the activity of those micro-organisms, which break down organic matter and release nutrients.

Underlying many of their alternative conceptions about global climate change, ozone layer depletion and acid deposition is a tendency for students to incorrectly associate a range of environmental pollutants with a specific type of environmental degradation. However, as Boyes and Stanisstreet argue (1996), there are additional reasons for these misconceptions which can include:

- The part the media plays in reporting issues to the general public. Sadly the coverage of such issues is not always accurate.

- The fact that the scientific community is still debating, revising and updating its ideas about the effects and the extent of the problems, making conceptualisation more difficult.

Although research into students' alternative conceptions has focused largely on acid deposition, ozone depletion and global climate change, other concerns have emerged. For example, Schibeci et al. (1993) studied students' ideas about water pollution and revealed uncertainty about eutrophication. The algae were variously identified as 'seaweed', 'bacteria', 'chemicals' and 'pollution'. Schibeci et al. (1993) also found that some students attributed the higher incidence of algae in winter to a more abundant water supply.

Other environmental topics worth investigating might include students' ideas about terms such as 'desertification', 'natural hazard' and the recently much publicised 'El Nino effect'.

Probing students' thinking on environmental ideas

A range of strategies can be used for gauging student ideas about environmental issues. Questionnaires like that shown in Figure 5 have traditionally played a part in these investigations. Another method is concept mapping. An example of how a concept map could be used to probe students' misconceptions about global climate change and ozone depletion is shown in Figure 6. For a full discussion of the nature, benefits and limitations of concept maps see Ruiz-Primo and Shavelson, 1996.

Having identified alternative conceptions in students' understanding of environmental issues teachers can then use their own knowledge and understanding of the topic to correct them. As the research into all of the environmental issues described above is ongoing the onus is on the teacher to remain 'in touch' with the debate and sufficiently abreast of conceptual developments to challenge students' alternative conceptions.

Figure 5: *Examples of question design.*

Example 1

Please indicate your response to the following statement about the greenhouse effect. Give reasons for your response in the large box.
A. Holes in the ozone layer will increase the greenhouse effect

agree ☐ →

disagree ☐ →

do not know ☐

Example 2

The most likely estimate for sea level rise by the year 2060 is

20cm ☐   40cm ☐   1m ☐   2m ☐   5m ☐

Example 3

Suggest reasons why the greenhouse effect might encourage plants to grow more vigorously.

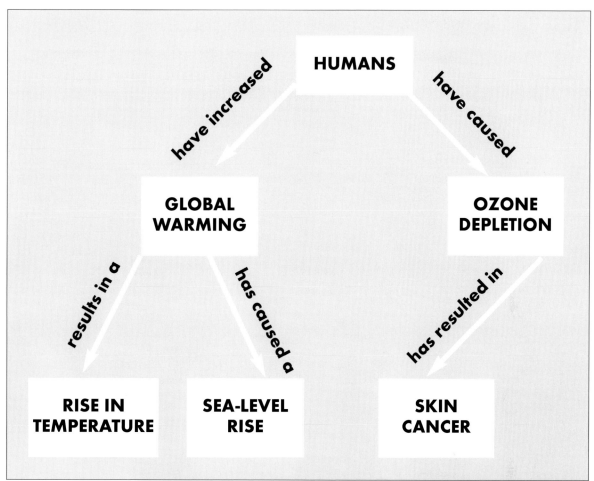

Figure 6: An example of a concept map. In constructing the map students might incorrectly link global climate change with ozone layer depletion. They may also suggest that humans cause global climate change, rather than enhancing an existing effect.

Key ideas

- Misconceptions have been identified about global climate change, ozone depletion and acid rain.

- Global climate change is commonly attributed to ozone layer depletion.

- There is considerable scope for investigating students' ideas about other topics such as El Niño.

- Questionnaires and concept mapping are useful techniques in identifying misconceptions.

- Up-to-date subject knowledge is essential if teachers are to challenge students' alternative conceptions.

Photo: Margaret Roberts

5: Pedagogical implications

What students already think and understand is the starting place for the introduction of new concepts in geography and from which conceptual understanding is developed. What teachers need to explore is why students have a particular understanding of key geographical concepts and where that understanding comes from. This information can provide a basis for challenging alternative conceptions and supporting students' understanding. This process should be seen as part of the continuing professional development of experienced, as well as novice teachers. By anticipating potential 'alternative conceptions', teachers can plan learning opportunities to develop students' understanding while avoiding, rather than compounding, misunderstandings. To avoid students confusing closely-related concepts (a common cause of misconceptions) use unambiguous words and expressions which accurately describe the subject matter (see also Dove, 1998a).

For learning to be a challenge, teachers need to encourage students to evaluate their ideas against hard evidence. Teachers can counter alternative conceptions by using a range of strategies in the geography classroom: for example, developing students' questioning skills, asking more open-ended questions, and extending their use of 'argument' as opposed to learning by 'consensus' (Lambert, 1997). This type of learning can only take place if teachers are clear themselves about the distinctions between key concepts. A degree in geography does not necessarily denote expert knowledge, and as 'expert knowledge' constantly changes, teachers must remain alert to developments in research in geography as well as in relevant fields.

Keeping a critical eye on all forms of teaching resources and constantly re-evaluating your teaching approach should ensure that students' alternative conceptions do not go unchallenged. Some of the contexts in which alternative conceptions may arise, and ways of dealing with them are described below.

Contexts

Teaching resources
Popular geography textbooks can be a source of misinformation and geographical inaccuracies. For example, Sparks has identified errors in students' understanding of plate tectonics:

'The main errors involved are the confusion of the Earth's crust with the plates and the absence of any definition or explanation of the term "lithosphere". The ocean crust and continental crust of the Earth are layers of distinct composition. They are parts of the great plates of the Earth, but are entirely unrelated to the concepts of lithospheric plates, and plate tectonics, which is fundamental to plate tectonics. A plate is defined as the cold outer layer of the earth which behaves in a rigid manner so that the earth's broken surface is broken up into plates. This layer is called the lithosphere and is defined and recognised on the basis of mechanical physical properties' (Sparks, 1999).

Sparks attributes these 'errors' to the confusion embedded in some geography textbooks and goes on to identify elements of the illustrations and text which he describes as 'confusing, inconsistent and in serious error'. Sparks refers specifically to the use of sial and sima concepts which, he states '... had been abandoned by earth scientists in the 1960s as these ideas were superseded by plate tectonics'. The consequence of this is that students' knowledge is based on dated information of key geographical concepts and their understanding of plate tectonics contains major errors. Such errors then feed into students' answers to questions during GCSE and post-16 examinations and into their undergraduate studies. This example indicates that the onus is on the geography teacher to critically evaluate resources such as textbooks from both the pedagogical and the geographical point of view. This can be done by asking: 'Does this resource support learning?' 'Is this resource interesting and well presented?' And, perhaps most importantly, 'Is the content correct?'

Photographs and images

Teachers and students should bear in mind that photographs in textbooks reflect the authors' or illustrators' stereotypical images. Their choice can lead students to believe that some physical features are the same the world over; whereas features such as beaches and valleys, for example, vary considerably in form. Teachers, therefore, need to provide students with a variety of different examples of each landform (see pages 21-22).

One example of a stereotypical image is the persistent appearance of the Niagara Falls as 'the example' waterfall in geography textbooks. As a consequence the Niagara Falls may unwittingly be 'over-quoted' by students in a range of different contexts such as coursework and examinations. This use of a single example does not necessarily indicate a clear understanding of what a waterfall is. What is important is that students should be able to transfer their understanding of a waterfall from the Niagara Falls to other contexts.

Another source for photographs used in geography classrooms are the 'idealised' photographs in glossy tourist brochures, designed to sell the destination to the public. Carefully-composed shots of the Grand Canyon, for instance, are often taken at sunrise or sunset when the colours in the landscape are more intense, but these photographs cannot and do not capture the third dimension or the scale of the Canyon. The use of any such image in the classroom needs to be evaluated and carefully planned into the lesson to ensure that students are not unwittingly left with an alternative conception which will prove difficult to challenge at a later date.

By encouraging students to draw on their life experiences beyond school teachers can make learning feel relevant to them. For example, teachers can ask students to obtain a selection of images which illustrate their conceptions of say, rivers and then 'check out' any misconceptions of rivers by looking at the appropriateness of each image. The teacher can also challenge any images which appear to be based on alternative conceptions. This approach enables teachers to attach new learning to students' existing cognitive framework.

The plus side of photographs is that they can be used to develop students' visual literacy skills and to encourage them to 'interrogate' images from a range of sources, including textbooks and brochures.

Fieldwork

A potentially interesting and useful fieldwork activity is to ask students to critically evaluate interpretative boards located near sites of geomorphological interest. An example of this type of activity (based on features found in Arizona and southern Utah, USA) is suggested in Dove (1998e). A-level students were invited to assess the success of interpretative boards Rainbow Bridge, the world's largest natural stone arch, and The Goosenecks, a set of incised meanders in explaining geomorphological features to the general public.

Students were also asked to design their own interpretative boards to explain the formation of *hoodoos* (earth pillars) at Bryce Canyon and the formation of mesas and buttes in Monument Valley. Although this activity was used in an international context the approach can be transferred to fieldwork with younger students in the UK. For example, the Giant's Causeway on the coast of County Antrim, Northern Ireland, is a popular tourist attraction, but without effective interpretative aids visitors may leave the site with little understanding of how the basalt columns formed. This type of fieldwork activity encourages students to question what they are reading and thus their understanding of the concepts/processes involved. The teacher should support the discussion in the field, between students and between student and teacher. This approach should enable the teacher to identify and challenge alternative conceptions as they arise.

With a range of possibilities from which to make rational choices, students can begin to question and perhaps adapt their conceptions in the field. For students this learning is more meaningful than that achieved by, for example, rote learning. It also ensures that the students have a sense of ownership of the fieldwork outcomes.

Practical demonstrations

Practical demonstration of concepts in the geography classroom can help develop understanding of concepts and change misconceptions related to specific issues. Research by Baxter (1989), for example, suggests that students have a variety of explanations for day and night: some recognise that this phenomenon is caused by the Earth spinning on its axis once every 24 hours, while others falsely believe day and night are the result of the sun travelling round the Earth or vice versa. One practical approach, which helps students to resolve this debate, is to provide them with models of the Earth and sun and ask them to consider which possibility is most likely, given the cycle takes only 24 hours.

A similar approach can be adopted to explore ideas about the seasons - a topic which Baxter (1989) and Mant and Summers (1993) have found students of all ages have difficulty explaining. They found that some students understand that the seasons are caused by the Earth's tilted axis moving round the sun, while others believe that winter and summer are the result of annual variations in the distance between these two bodies. Given a globe tilted on its axis and a 'model' of the sun, with the information that the northern and southern hemispheres experience winter and summer at different times, students could be asked to consider which of the possible explanations was more likely.

Open-ended questioning

The use of appropriate questions can go a long way to counter alternative conceptions. These can be related to specific issues on which students hold misconceptions: for example, evidence suggests that students commonly incorrectly identify rock types because their judgements are based on stereotypical images of colour. Students frequently confuse white or yellow varieties of sandstone with limestone or assume that all sandstones are orange and, therefore, do not recognise the white and brown varieties (Dove, 1996a). One way to counter this misconception would be to provide students with a variety of different examples of limestone and sandstone, but this would only increase their knowledge of known rock types. A better approach is to encourage students to devise questions which will help them to discriminate between two rock types and apply the questions to a range of specimens. For example: 'Does limestone have a significantly higher fossil content than sandstone?', 'Do the rock types react differently to dilute hydrochloric acid?'

As identified on page 12, a further common cause of misconception is for students to assume that landforms of similar appearance have one origin. Again teachers can discourage this belief by asking more open-ended questions when a topic is introduced. During a lesson on the formation of rapids, if a teacher shows students photographs of the feature and asks closed questions (e.g. 'What is obstructing the flow of water in the river?'), students will probably respond with 'A resistant band of rock'. (Although many rapids are formed in this way, some develop when a waterfall migrates upstream, while others occur where debris fans (deposited during flash-floods from side-canyons) fail to be removed by the main channel, as in the Colorado.) A more opened-ended question, e.g. 'What do you see in the picture?', followed by 'How did the rocks get there?', will allow the students to respond with a variety of explanations.

Teaching argument

The term 'argument' here refers to purposeful procedure or activity. Teaching students to use 'argument' as part of their reasoning is another strategy for dispelling their misconceptions about geographical concepts. Students need to be taught 'argument' in the same way they need to be taught other mental skills (see Andrews, 1993). Often students are given the 'consensus view' - for example, of desert processes or global climate change - without addressing the arguments. Students need to recognise that what is 'consensus' today may become a 'misconception' tomorrow. This can be illustrated by the example of desert varnish. Desert varnish was originally thought to form when iron and manganese were drawn to the surface and oxidised, but this belief was challenged when the varnish was found on rocks with a low manganese and iron content. Current theory suggests that desert varnish forms when wind-blown manganese and iron-rich clays are deposited on rocks dampened by dew, where the presence of bacteria and lichen on the surface of the rocks helps fix the elements to the stone (Cooke *et al.*, 1992). To encourage students to think about this concept, ask them to suggest possible explanations for desert varnish from a description. When they have done so tell them that varnish occurs on rocks of low manganese and iron content and ask them if they wish to revise their original ideas in the light of this information.

Another issue which could be debated in the geography classroom is the effects of global climate change. Ten years ago some scientists predicted that global climate change would lead to a 5m rise in sea-levels and at one time scientists believed that Antarctica was too cold to be altered by global climate change. Original estimates of sea-level rise have now been reduced and recent research revealed that the Riiser-Larsen Ice Shelf which borders the Atlantic Ocean and Weddell Sea is disappearing. Students might debate this topic by evaluating the evidence used to make the original predictions and considering what changes occurred to make scientists revise their estimates.

These examples indicate the need to be aware of new evidence on specific topics. The evidence may consolidate or challenge existing understanding of the concept and consequently arguments need to be fully debated before a consensus is reached.

What is in it for me?

Both you and your students are likely to benefit from the information you can gather on alternative conceptions. The data collection methods need not be sophisticated to be useful. For example, a ten-minute activity exploring perceptions at the beginning of a lesson may reveal ideas which you had not considered before. As a consequence, you may re-examine your own understanding and try to improve on it. You may seek explanations for your own perceptions and decide next time the topic is introduced to present it in a different way.

It is important to disseminate findings to a wider teaching audience. Not only would this benefit students, but you may well discover that you hold some of the alternative ideas which have been identified in students. I would welcome feedback via the GA of any students' alternative conceptions you have observed. Alternatively, you may like to consider submitting articles to *Teaching Geography*. There is also considerable scope for research into specific alternative conceptions at degree and post-graduate level. All of these activities contribute to the continual professional development of all teachers.

Key ideas

- Teacher use of ambiguous and inaccurate language can help to produce students' alternative conceptions.

- Textbook photographs and other images need to be used selectively and critically.

- Alternative conceptions can be challenged by developing students' skills in a variety of contexts, e.g. using questions during fieldwork and practical demonstrations.

- The teaching of 'argument', rather than learning by 'consensus', encourages students to confront their alternative ideas.

Photo: Margaret Roberts

6: Conclusion

The investigation of alternative conceptions in physical, natural and environmental geography has the potential to significantly improve teaching and learning. The recognition of stereotypes in our perceptions of landscapes and natural environments, although not necessarily incorrect in themselves, will increase awareness of examples in different settings.

There is considerable potential to investigate alternative perceptions in human as well as physical geography. How, for example, are 'green belts' perceived? Are they regarded as pristine, rural environments, or do students realise that many include derelict buildings and overgrown set- aside land? How do students perceive developing cities? Are they just a collection of shanty towns? Why do students draw the Equator through the Sahara? Likewise, mapping misconceptions can be discussed in relation to specific questions. Some students' mapping misconceptions have been discussed by Barratt and Barratt Hacking (1998), but much work still needs to be done in this field.

Many of the techniques used here to identify alternative conceptions can also be applied when teaching other subjects. For example, drawing can be used in biology to indicate how students perceive the carbon or nitrogen cycles. Concept mapping can be used to identify relationships between events in history.

As discussed in the previous chapter, teachers as well as students stand to gain in the identification and explanation of alternative conceptions. Research in this field has taught me to examine my own understanding of topics more carefully. I strive for greater precision when giving definitions and explaining concepts. I hesitate to make assumptions about colour, shape and appearance when examining landforms. I view textbook illustrations more critically, looking for diagrams which deceive and photographs which reinforce stereotypes. I would argue that through skilful questioning it is possible for teachers to lead students to more accurate conceptions of key geographical features and to provide them with a framework for future analysis. This approach should result in students having a more accurate understanding of geography and individuals who can transfer their critical skills to other life contexts.

Bibliography

Agassiz, L. (1838) 'Upon glaciers, moraines and erratic blocks', *Edinburgh New Philosophical Journal*, 24, p. 381.

Anderson, S. and Moss, B. (1993) 'How wetland habitats are perceived by children: consequences for children's education and wetland conservation', *International Journal of Science Education*, 15, 5, pp. 473-85.

Andrews, R. (1993) *Improving the Quality of Arguments 5-16*. Hull: Centre for Studies in Rhetoric.

Aron, R.H., Francek, M.A., Nelson, B.D. and Bisard, W.J. (1994) 'Atmospheric misconceptions', *The Science Teacher*, 61, 1, pp. 31-3.

Ausubel, D.P. (1968) *Educational Psychology: A cognitive view*. New York: Holt, Rinehart & Winston.

Barman, C.R., Griffiths, A.K. and Okebukola, P.A.O. (1995) 'High school students' concepts regarding food chains and food webs: a multinational study', *International Journal of Science Education*, 17, 6, pp. 775-82.

Barratt, R. and Barratt Hacking, E. (1998) 'Researching how geography teachers can help students overcome mapping misconceptions', *Teaching Geography*, 23, 2, pp. 88-90.

Baxter, J. (1989) 'Children's understanding of familiar astronomical events', *International Journal of Science Education*, 11, 5, pp. 502-13.

Boyes, E. and Stanisstreet, M. (1992) 'Students' perceptions of global warming', *International Journal of Environmental Studies*, 42, pp. 287-300.

Boyes, E. and Stanisstreet, M. (1997) 'The environmental impact of cars: children's ideas and reasoning', *Environmental Education Research*, 3, 3, pp. 269-82.

Boyes, E., Chambers, W. and Stanisstreet, M. (1995) 'Trainee primary teachers' ideas about the ozone layer', *Environmental Education Research*, 1, 2, pp. 133-45.

Boyes, E., Chambers, W. and Stanisstreet, M. (1996) 'Threats to the global atmospheric environment: the extent of pupil understanding', *International Journal of Geography and Geographical Education Research*, 5, 3, pp. 186-95.

Carlston, C.W. (1969) 'Downstream variations in the hydraulic geometry of streams: special emphasis on mean velocity', *American Journal of Science*, 267, pp. 499-510.

Christidou, V. and Koulaidis, V. (1996) 'Children's models of ozone layer and ozone depletion', *Research in Science Education*, 26, 4, pp. 421-36.

Clowes A. and Comfort, P. (1982) *Process and Landform*. Edinburgh: Oliver & Boyd.

Collard, R. (1988) *The Physical Geography of Landscape*. London: Unwin Hyman.

Cooke, R., Goudie, A. and Warren, A. (1992) *Desert Geomorphology*. London: UCL Press.

Davis, W.H. (1899) 'The geographical cycle', *Geographical Journal*, 14, pp. 481-504.

Department for Education and Science (1995) *Geography in the National Curriculum (England)*. London: HMSO.

Dove, J.E. (1996a) 'Student identification of rock types', *Journal of Geoscience Education*, 44, 3, pp. 266-9.

Dove, J.E. (1996b) 'Student misconceptions on the greenhouse effect, ozone layer depletion and acid rain', *Environmental Education Research*, 2, 1, pp. 89-100.

Dove, J.E. (1997a) 'Student ideas about weathering and erosion', *International Journal of*

Science Education, 19, 8, pp. 971-80.

Dove, J.E. (1997b) 'Do polar bears live in Antarctica?', *Journal of Biological Education*, 31, 1, pp. 3-6.

Dove, J.E. (1997c) 'Student preferences in the depiction of the water-cycle and selected landforms', *International Research in Geographical and Environmental Education*, 6, 2, pp. 135-47.

Dove, J.E. (1998a) 'Students' alternative conceptions in Earth science: a review of research and implications for teaching and learning', *Research Papers in Education*, 13, 2, pp. 183-201.

Dove, J.E. (1998b) 'Alternative conceptions about the weather', *School Science Review*, 79, 289, pp. 65-9.

Dove, J.E. (1998c) 'Students' ideas about limestone denudation', unpublished manuscript, University of Exeter.

Dove, J.E. (1998d) 'Students' perceptions of deserts', unpublished manuscript, University of Exeter.

Dove, J.E. (1998e) 'Explaining geomorphological features to the public: an A-level activity', *Teaching Geography*, 23, 2, pp. 93-7.

Dove, J.E., Everett, L.A. and Preece, P.F.W. (in press) 'View from the river bank: the urban child's conception of a river', *Education 3-13*.

Driver, R. and Easley, J. (1978) 'Pupils and paradigms: A review of literature related to concept development in adolescent science students', *Studies in Science Education*, 5, pp. 61-84.

Driver, R., Guesne, E. and Tiberghien, A. (1985) *Children's Ideas in Science*. Milton Keynes: Open University Press.

Elsom, D. (1991) *Atmospheric Pollution*. Oxford: Blackwell.

Fisher, K. and Lipson, J. (1986) 'Twenty questions about student errors', *Journal of Research in Science Teaching*, 23, pp. 783-803.

Goudie, A. (1995) *The Changing Earth: Rates of geomorphological processes*. Oxford: Blackwell.

Goudie, A., Atkinson, B.W., Gregory, K.J., Simmons, I.G., Stoddart, D.R. and Sugden, D. (eds) (1994) *The Encyclopedic Dictionary of Physical Geography*. Oxford: Blackwell.

Greaves, E., Stanisstreet, M., Boyes, E. and Williams, T. (1993) 'Children's ideas about rain forests', *Journal of Biological Education*, 27, 3, pp. 189-94.

Herzog, T.R. (1985) 'A cognitive analysis of preferences for waterscapes', *Journal of Environmental Psychology*, 5, 3, pp. 225-42.

Jennings, T. (1989) *Deserts*. Oxford: Oxford University Press.

Jennings, T. (1993) *Rivers*. Oxford: Oxford University Press.

Johnson, P. and Gott, R. (1996) 'Constructivism and evidence from children's ideas', *Science Education*, 80, 5, pp. 561-77.

Kuiper, J. (1994) 'Student ideas of science concepts: alternative frameworks', *International Journal of Science Education*, 16, 3, pp. 279-92.

Lambert, D. (1997) 'Opening minds' in Slater, F., Lambert, D. and Lines, D. (eds) *Education, Environment and Economy: Reporting research in a new academic grouping* (Bedford Day Papers). London: Institute of Education, University of London.

Mant, J. and Summers, M. (1993) 'Some primary-school teachers' understanding of the Earth's place in the universe', *Research Papers in Education*, 8, 1, pp. 101-26.

Milne, A.A. (1973) *The House at Pooh Corner*. London: Methuen.

Moyle, R. (1980) 'Weather', *Learning in Science Project Working Paper 21*. Hamilton: University of Waikato, New Zealand.

Nelson, B.D., Aron, R.H. and Francek, M.A. (1992) 'Clarification of selected misconceptions in physical geography', *Journal of Geography*, 91, 2, pp. 76-80.

Osborne, R.J., Bell, B.F. and Gilbert, J.K. (1983) 'Science teaching and children's views of the world', *European Journal of Science Education*, 5, 1, pp. 1-14.

Piaget, J. (1929) *The Child's Conception of the World*. London: Routledge & Kegan Paul.

Piaget, J. (1930) *The Child's Conception of Physical Causality*. London: Kegan Paul/Trench, Trubner & Co.

Preece, P.F.W. (1978) 'Exploration of semantic space: a review of research on the organisation of scientific concepts in semantic memory', *Science Education*, 63, pp. 547-62.

Ruiz-Primo, M.A. and Shavelson, R.J. (1996) 'Problems and issues in the use of concept maps in Science assessment', *Journal of Research in Science Teaching*, 33, 6, pp. 569-600.

Schibeci, R.A., Fetherstonhaugh, A. and Griffin, S. (1993) 'Conceptions of water-related phenomena', *Research in Science Education*, 23, pp. 259-65.

Solomon, J. (1994) 'The rise and fall of constructivism', *Studies in Science Education*, 22, pp. 1-19

Sparks, S. (1999) personal communication with Geographical Association.

Strommen, E. (1995) 'Lions and tigers and bears. Oh my! Children's conceptions of forests and their inhabitants', *Journal of Research in Science Education*, 32, 7, pp. 683-98.

Teacher Training Agency (1997) *Standards for the Award of Qualified Teacher Status*. London: TTA.

Trudgill, S.T. (1985) *Limestone Geomorphology*. London: Longman.

Viles, H. (1993) 'Caves, cones and carbonation', *Geography Review*, 6, 5, pp. 17-21.

Waugh, D. (1990) *Geography: An integrated approach*. Andover: Thomas Nelson.

White, R.T. and Gunstone, R. (1992) *Probing Understanding*. New York: Falmer Press.

Whittow, J. (1984) *Dictionary of Physical Geography*. London: Penguin.